A PUPIL'S WORKBOOK OF ACTIVITIES
USING EVERYDAY MATERIALS

Investigating Home Economics

Margaret Barlow

formerly Head of Home Economics Department, Finham Park Comprehensive School, Coventry

Philip Barlow

Senior Lecturer, Department of Science Education, University of Warwick

M

Macmillan Education
London & Basingstoke

First published 1983
Reprinted 1984

Published by
Macmillan Education Ltd
Houndmills Basingstoke Hampshire RG21 2XS
and London
Associated companies throughout the world

Printed in Hong Kong

British Library Cataloguing in Publication Data

Barlow, Margaret
    Investigating home economics.
    1. Home economics
    I. Title   II. Barlow, Philip
    640   TX167

    ISBN 0-333-28398-8

Contents

Introduction

'Investigating' means examining and finding out as much as possible about something. In Home Economics the materials which can be investigated include FOOD and FABRIC.

During an investigation it may be necessary to use several methods, such as:

LOOKING   SMELLING   FEELING   LISTENING
TASTING (but only if you *know* it is a FOOD) COMPARING
WEIGHING   MEASURING   CRUSHING   MIXING
STRETCHING   MAGNIFYING   HEATING   BURNING

and, of course, READING what others have found out and might be helpful to know!

The results of an investigation can be collected together and recorded by

WRITING   TABULATING   DRAWING   TAPE RECORDING

Choose any suitable methods for the investigations in this book.

Safety first!

Always READ and follow the instructions in this book carefully. HOT, SHARP, BREAKABLE and FLAMMABLE materials can be dangerous if handled carelessly.

Avoid accidents by working sensibly.

Follow these rules:
   Ask for help if in doubt.
   Work tidily.
   Wipe up any spills immediately.
   Keep the floor dry and free of all obstructions.
   Tie long hair back.
   Wear an apron or overall to cover loose clothing.

Abbreviations

g   = gram
kg = kilogram
mm = millimetre
cm = centimetre
m   = metre
ml = millilitre
min = minutes
tsp = teaspoonful (level)

Part 1: Food

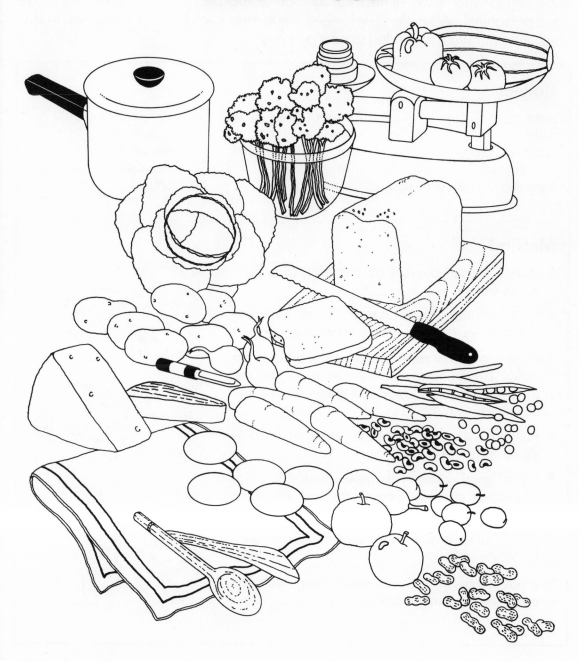

1 What is needed for washing-up?

Dirty crockery and cutlery can cause illness as well as being unpleasant to use. It is important to wash away all traces of food or harmful bacteria might grow and cause 'food poisoning'. Washing-up will need doing after each Food Investigation in this book. Find out what is needed to do it properly.

Collect

plate	2 teaspoons	liquid washing-up
knife	margarine	detergent
washing-up bowl	cooking oil (or melted	tea towel
draining rack	margarine)	dish cloth
2 small glass basins or jugs		

Method

1 Spread a small amount of margarine on a plate with a knife.

2 Hold the greasy plate and knife under a running cold tap. Fig. 1. Look carefully at what happens.

3 Place the greasy plate and knife in a bowl of hot water. After one minute remove them and put them in the draining rack. Leave the water in the bowl to go cold. Fig. 2.

4 Half fill a basin with cold water, add ½ tsp of cooking oil and stir well.

5 Half fill another basin with hot water, add ½ tsp of cooking oil, stir well. Compare the contents of the two basins. Fig. 3.

6 Add a squeeze of washing-up detergent to each basin and stir again.

7 Empty both basins and leave them with the spoons to drain in the rack.

Fig. 1

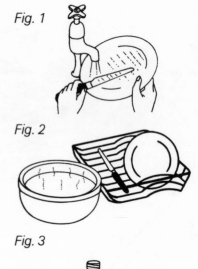

Fig. 2

Fig. 3

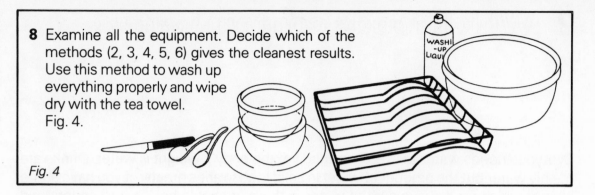

8 Examine all the equipment. Decide which of the methods (2, 3, 4, 5, 6) gives the cleanest results. Use this method to wash up everything properly and wipe dry with the tea towel. Fig. 4.

Fig. 4

Questions

1 Which foods are likely to leave grease on crockery and cutlery?

2 Why is grease difficult to wash off? (The experiment in Further Work will help to answer this question.)

3 What other types of 'dirt' might need washing off crockery and cutlery?

4 How can a dish cloth help when washing-up?

5 Is it best to leave washed dishes to dry in a rack or to use a tea towel? Give reasons.

6 Would rinsing in clear water before draining or drying washed dishes give better results? Try it.

7 After a meal, in what order should the following be washed: saucepans, plates, cutlery, cups and saucers, baking dishes, tumblers? Why?

8 What are 'pan scrubbers'? When would they be used?

Further work

1 (a) Set up equipment as in the diagram. Fig. 5.
Look carefully at the screen at each stage of the experiment.

(b) Put some cold water in one petri dish and hot water in the other.

(c) Add a few drops of cooking oil to each dish and stir with the glass rods.

(d) Add a small squeeze of washing-up detergent to each dish and stir again.

From what you have seen explain why hot water and detergent are needed for washing-up.

2 Make a list of brands of washing-up detergents and compare their prices.

3 Do a survey of washing-up habits among friends and neighbours. Make charts to show results.

4 Find advertisements and information about automatic dishwashers.

Fig. 5

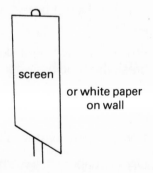

petri dish and glass rod

overhead projector

screen

or white paper on wall

Washing-up is a rather tedious but necessary chore. How will you make sure it is well done?

2 Which foods contain water?

Everyone needs water to live. Two-thirds of the body's weight is water. Drinks are mainly water but the amount of water in solid foods varies greatly. If you have some idea of which foods have a lot of water in them, it should help you to understand some of the changes that happen when they are stored or cooked.

Collect

filter papers (or blotting paper)
mortar and pestle
teaspoon

small amounts of several foods, including bread, some fruits, vegetables and store cupboard ingredients (e.g. rice)

washing-up equipment
vegetable knife
pencil

Method

1 Pour 1 tsp water on to the centre of a filter paper (or 15 cm square of blotting paper). Keep this paper and use it as a 'control' to compare with all the other tests.

Fig. 1

2 Label filter papers in pencil with the names of the foods to be tested, one for each food.

3 With dry hands and using clean, dry equipment for each one, cut up and/or crush a small amount of each food. Use the mortar and pestle for crushing. Fig. 1. Place 1 tsp of each food on its labelled paper.

4 Fold over each filter paper and gently but firmly press the food between the paper. Fig. 2.

Fig. 2

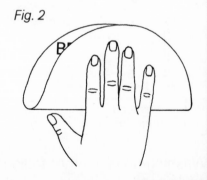

5 Unfold and carefully scrape the food off the papers.

6 Compare the 'wetness' of the papers.

7 Dry the papers in a warm place.

8 Wash up.

Fig. 3   *Fig. 4*

lemon squeezer

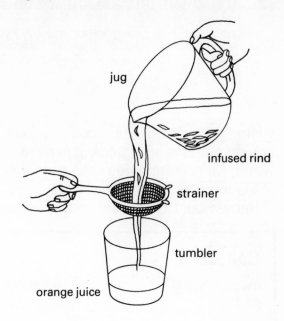

jug

infused rind

strainer

tumbler

orange juice

Questions

1 Which were the 'wettest' foods?
2 Which were the 'driest' foods?
3 Look at the dried papers. What happened to the 'wet' patches?
4 Was all the 'liquid' in foods water? Give reasons for the answer.
5 Which foods can be drunk?
6 What are 'dehydrated' foods? Make a list of examples.
7 Which of the foods tested could be stored for a long time?
8 Which ones will spoil if they are not eaten while they are fresh? What might happen to them?

Further work

1 Strongly flavoured watery foods can be 'diluted' with more water. Make a drink by diluting the juice of an orange. Fig. 3. Extra colour and flavour can be given to the drink by 'infusing' the thin outer layer of the orange rind in hot water. When this liquid is cool it can be strained and added to orange juice. Fig. 4.
2 What is a 'concentrated' liquid? Name some foods which are concentrated liquids and explain how they could be used in meals.
3 Food is sometimes cooked in water. What are the names given to 'wet' methods of cooking? Describe the equipment used for cooking food in water.
4 Find out about the kind of food eaten by astronauts when flying in space. Why do they have to have special foods?

Which foods do you think may need water added to them before they are eaten?

3 How much water is needed to make kedgeree?

Water is essential when cooking food. It is used for cleaning hands, food and equipment. It is an ingredient in many recipes. Some foods are actually cooked in water. Making kedgeree uses quite a lot of water. Keep a record of how much, by measuring the volume of all water used.

Remember to stand the measuring jug on a flat surface when reading the level.

Collect

measuring jug   tablespoon   mixing bowl
scales   serving dish   washing-up equipment

A	B	C	D
50 g long grain rice	1 egg	small 'Boil-in-the-Bag' pack of smoked fish	sprigs of fresh parsley
1 tsp salt	small saucepan		paper towel
saucepan	draining spoon	saucepan	sheet of newspaper
sieve	chopping board	kitchen scissors	chopping board
kettle	table knife	plate, knife and fork	cook's knife, teaspoon

Work in a group of four using one cooker and a sink. *Fig. 1*
Choose between yourselves who is to be **A**, **B**, **C** and **D**.

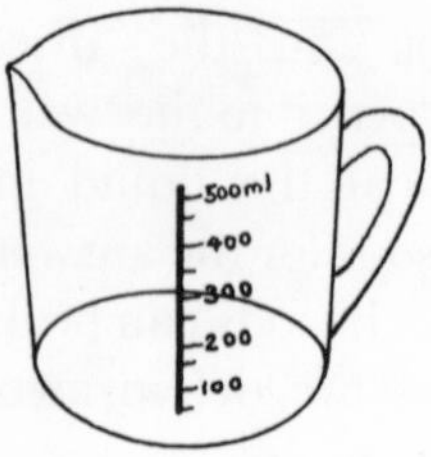

Method

1 Copy out this chart:

	litres	millilitres
Washing hands		
Cooking rice		
Rinsing rice		
Boiling egg		
Cooling egg		
Cooking fish		
Rinsing fishy plate		
Washing parsley		
Washing-up		
TOTAL		

Fig. 2

2 Measure ALL the water used by everyone in the group and fill in the chart as each measurement is made. Fig. 1.

3A (1) Half fill the saucepan with water. Put to boil.
(2) When boiling add the rice and salt.
(3) Stirring occasionally, boil until the rice is tender, 15–20 minutes.
(4) Boil a kettle of water.
(5) Strain the rice through the sieve.
(6) Rinse the rice, in the sieve, with the boiled water. Fig. 2.

3B (1) Put the egg in the saucepan, cover with cold water.
(2) Put the pan on a high heat until the water is boiling.
(3) Continue boiling for 10 minutes.
(4) Lift out the egg, empty the saucepan and refill with cold water.
(5) Put the egg to cool in the cold water.
(6) Remove the shell and chop the egg.

Fig. 3

3C (1) Following the instructions on the packet, cook the fish.
(2) Empty the contents of the bag on to the plate.
(3) Using the knife and fork remove skin and bones. Break up the fish into flakes. Fig. 3.
(4) Put the fish in the mixing bowl. Rinse the fishy plate with hot water.

3D (1) Wash the parsley in cold water. Dry it.
(2) Remove any thick stalks and chop the parsley finely.
(3) Put 2 heaped tsps parsley in the mixing bowl.
(4) Wrap *all* rubbish (from **B**, **C**, **D**) in newspaper and throw away.

4 Mix the boiled rice and chopped egg with the fish and parsley and put the KEDGEREE on the serving dish.
5 Wash up.

Questions

1 How much water was used?
2 Why was there not much water left in the pan when the rice finished cooking?
3 Why was the cooked rice rinsed?
4 Why should freshly boiled water from the cold tap be used for cooking rather than water from the hot tap?
5 Why put the boiled egg in cold water?
6 Why are some foods 'Boil-in-the-Bag'?
7 Why did the fishy plate need rinsing before it was washed?
8 Why did the parsley need washing?
9 What had happened to the insides of the saucepans during the cooking?
10 How were the saucepans cleaned?

Further work

1 What safety precautions are necessary when using pans on a cooker hob?
2 Work out some menus for complete meals which include kedgeree.
3 Look for other recipes for kedgeree and suggest how this one could be altered or improved.
4 Find out how fish is smoked. Why is it done?
5 About one hundred years ago, when rich people employed a lot of servants, kedgeree might have been served for breakfast. Find out what life would have been like for a rich family in those days.

Water is often taken for granted. Make a list of all the ways it is used at home.

4 Why should food in a refrigerator be covered?

A cool refrigerator helps to prevent fresh food going bad quickly. Unless it is automatically defrosted (when a trickle of water collects in a tray at the back of the cabinet and evaporates) ice collects round the freezing compartment. See if you can work out where this ice comes from.

Collect

2 tea plates	chopping board	2 cm cube margarine
small glass basin	2 small eggs	plastic wrapping film
saucer	small onion	washing-up equipment
knife		

Set up these experiments during one lesson. It is best if the refrigerator has been defrosted. From the results, answer the questions the following week.

Fig. 1

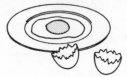

Method

1 Carefully crack the eggs, remove their shells and put one egg on each of the plates.

2 Leave one egg uncovered. Fig. 1.

3 Cover the other egg with the basin inverted. Fig. 2.

Fig. 2

4 Place both plates side by side on a shelf in the refrigerator. Leave for about a week.

5 Peel the onion and slice it on the chopping board.

6 Place the margarine and onion slices on the saucer. Take care not to let them touch each other. Fig. 3.

Fig. 3

7 Cover the saucer with plastic wrapping film. Put in the refrigerator. Leave for about a week.

8 Wash up.

Fig. 4

Questions

1 What has happened to the eggs? Describe the difference between the un-covered egg and the covered egg.

2 Uncover the saucer. Take care not to touch the onion. Move the margarine to another saucer. Smell it. Taste it. What has happened to the margarine?

3 Is there any 'frost' round the freezing compartment of the refrigerator? If so, what is it and where has it come from?

4 What are three important reasons for covering food in a refrigerator?

Further work

1 Collect different materials which could be used to cover or wrap food in a re-frigerator. Find out which keep foods moist the longest. (Small 'bread parcels' might be an idea to try.)

2 Using a thermometer compare the tem-perature inside a refrigerator with room temperature.

3 Find pictures of different types of re-frigerators and their prices.

4 Make a list of reasons for using a re-frigerator.

How can food be spoilt by storing it in a refrigerator?

5 How acid is food?

Some very acid foods can be recognised by their sourness. However, it is not always possible to tell how acid a food is by its flavour and pH paper gives a more accurate result. When cooking it may be useful to know that very acid foods will curdle milk. Jam sets well when made with very acid fruit. Baking powder is a mixture of an acid and an alkali.

Collect

mortar and pestle	Universal Indicator papers	small amounts of a wide
saucer	(pH 1–11) with colour	range of foods and store
teaspoon	chart	cupboard ingredients
pins	Jif lemon	including fruits,
sheet of plain white paper	washing-up equipment	vegetables, sugar, salt
		and baking powder

WARNINGS: Hands MUST BE DRY every time the indicator paper is touched.
ALL equipment must be RINSED and DRIED between each test.

Method

Fig. 1

1 Prepare a chart on the plain paper.

food	indicator paper	pH

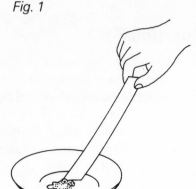

2 On a saucer mix ½ tsp sugar with 1 tsp cold water. Take a piece of indicator paper and dip one end in the mixture. Fig. 1.

3 Compare the colour of the wet end of the paper with the colour chart and decide the pH. Pin the indicator paper to the chart and fill in the details.

4 Rinse and dry all the equipment used.

5 Repeat 2, 3 and 4 for each food, using the mortar and pestle to crush those which are too solid to mix with water (e.g. carrots). Fig. 2.

Fig. 2

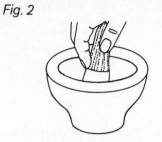

6 Spit on to the saucer and test saliva BUT throw this paper away after deciding the pH. Rinse the saucer.

7 Wash up.

Questions

1–6	pH7	8–14
increasingly ←—	—→	increasingly
acidic		alkaline

1 Using the chart above, make a list of the foods tested in order of their pH, starting with the most acidic.
2 What is the word that would describe a food which is neither an acid nor an alkali? (i.e. pH7).
3 Which foods were not acids?
4 Strongly acidic foods taste sour. Make a list of examples of things to eat which have a sour taste.
5 Sugar is often added to make sour foods more pleasant to eat. Does it make the foods less acidic? Check the answer with pH paper by testing a mixture of lemon juice and sugar.
6 What will happen to acidic foods when they are chewed?

Further work

1 Find out whether tap water is acid. Is freshly boiled water any more or less acid than tap water?
2 Which part of the tongue can taste sourness best – the tip, sides, centre or back?
3 Look at the lists of ingredients on packets, jars and tins in the food cupboard. Which ones contain acids?
4 It is sometimes said that 'acids attack tooth enamel'. If this is true how can it be prevented?

Fig. 3

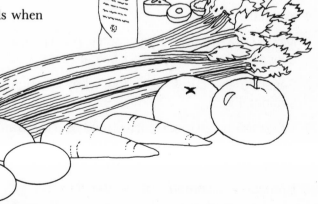

'Food poisoning' bacteria grow most easily in warm, moist foods which are not very acid. Which foods should be stored in a refrigerator to keep them safe to eat? (Results from Investigation 2 may help to answer this question.)

6 How is cheese made?

Cheese may have been discovered accidentally over a thousand years ago. It is thought it was probably first made when milk was carried in a bag made from the stomach of an animal. When you have tried making some cheese perhaps you will know whether this explanation is possible.

Collect

measuring jug	teaspoon	rennet
2 basins	knife	white vinegar
2 nylon strainers	shallow dish	salt
milk pan	300 ml fresh or pasteurised	stirring thermometer
small wooden spoon	milk	washing-up equipment

Method

1 Heat 150 ml milk to 37°C. Fig. 1.

2 Make 'junket' by stirring 1 tsp rennet into the warm milk.

3 Pour the junket into a shallow dish and leave in a warm place until set. (It may take about an hour to set, so could be made beforehand.)

4 Wash the pan.

5 Mix 150 ml milk with 2 tsp vinegar in the pan; stir over a low heat until the milk curdles.

6 Separate the curds from the whey through a strainer. Fig. 2.

7 When the junket is set, cut it up and pour it into another strainer. Stir the curds gently until no more whey runs through into the basin. Fig. 3.

8 Compare the contents of the strainers.

9 Discard the whey.

10 Mix both lots of curd together in a basin.

Fig. 1

low heat

Fig. 2

whey

11 Taste the curd 'cheese'; add a pinch of salt and taste again.

12 Heat half the 'cheese' gently until more whey runs from it. Strain again.

13 Compare the two samples of cheese for quantity, colour, texture and flavour.

14 Wash up.

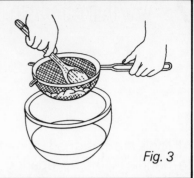

Fig. 3

Questions

1 How can 'curds and whey' be made?
2 Why is salt added to cheese?
3 How could soft curd cheese be made into a more solid type of cheese?
4 Inside everyone's stomach is gastric juice. This juice contains a substance similar to rennet and an acid. What must happen to milk after it has been drunk?
5 Find out the meaning of the word 'coagulation'. What was used to coagulate milk in this investigation?

Further work

1 Find out what happens when milk goes sour.
2 What can be done to milk to prevent it going sour?
3 Find out how Cheddar cheese is made.
4 Make a list of the names of British and foreign cheeses.
5 Explain how cheeses, all made from milk, can have different colours, textures and flavours.
6 Refer to Investigation 5 and work out which foods could not be used to flavour milk because they would cause curdling.

Fig. 4

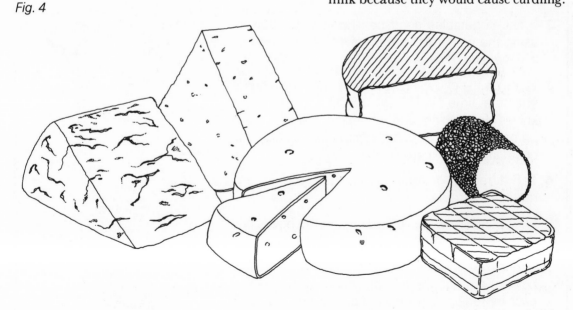

Cottage cheese used to be made by leaving milk to go sour. The curds were drained by suspending them in a muslin bag. Why is this not done nowadays?

7 Which knife is best?

All tools are designed for particular jobs. Their shape and size should be comfortable to handle. When preparing food to eat, the work will be easier and safer if the correct tool is used. Making an interesting salad is a good way of comparing different types of sharp tools.

Collect

salad ingredients for
  (1) slicing (e.g. tomato, cucumber, orange)
  (2) shredding or chopping (e.g. cabbage, nuts, parsley)
(3) grating (e.g. carrot, cheese)
paper towels
chopping board
vegetable peeler
a selection of sharp knives
different types of graters
small bowls for each ingredient
salad bowl or platter
washing-up equipment

Method

1 Wash all vegetables in cold water, dry them with paper towels.

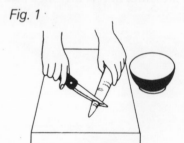

Fig. 1

2 If any vegetables need peeling (e.g. carrots) try using the peeler and small knives. Wrap peelings in paper and throw away.

3 Work on the chopping board. Prepare one ingredient at a time. VERY CAREFULLY try different knives for slicing and chopping, placing each prepared food in a separate bowl. Fig. 1. Wipe the board after each ingredient.

Fig. 2

4 Try different graters, using their coarse and medium cutters.

5 Look carefully at the ingredients in the bowls and decide which tools give the best results.

6 Either mix all the ingredients together in a salad bowl or arrange them neatly on a platter keeping each ingredient in a separate pile or row. Fig. 2.

7 If the salad cannot be eaten immediately, cover it and put in a refrigerator. Wash up.

Fig. 3

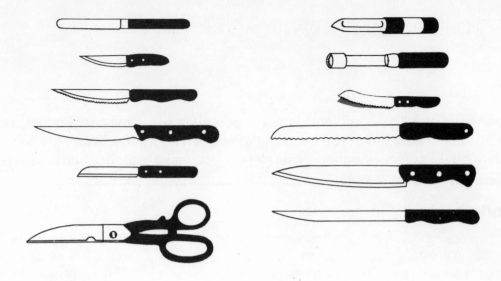

Questions

1 Which tools are best for (a) peeling (b) slicing (c) chopping?
2 Why do some knives have serrated blades?
3 What are the advantages of using a vegetable peeler?
4 Which graters are (a) easiest to use (b) easiest to clean?
5 What are the names of all the tools in the illustrations?
6 How should a cook's knife be held to make it safe for chopping?
7 Why is it necessary to wash vegetables before peeling, slicing, chopping or grating them?
8 How can accidents be avoided when using sharp tools?

Further work

1 Look around the kitchen and in hardware shops for unusual 'food-cutting' tools; describe them and say what they could be used for.
2 Find out how kitchen knives can be kept sharp.
3 What materials are used in making knives?
4 Sheffield is a city which is famous for making cutlery. Find out about this industry.

Do you agree that good tools might help you to become a good cook? If so, why?

8 How much waste is there when potatoes are peeled?

Accurate weighing of ingredients is not important in some recipes. But unless you have an idea of how much you are going to waste it might be difficult to know how much to buy! Practice weighing accurately as you make a cheese and potato pie.

Collect

kitchen scales	saucepan with lid	about ½ kg potatoes
scrubbing brush	small pie dish	salt
paper towels	teaspoon	25 g margarine
vegetable peeler	grater	50 g cheese
vegetable knife	potato masher	washing-up equipment
large basin	fork	

Method

1 Weigh the potatoes accurately. Fig. 1.

Fig. 1

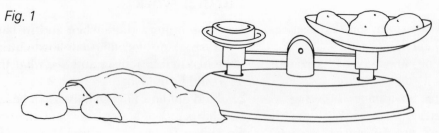

2 Scrub them under the cold running tap, dry them on paper towels, re-weigh them.

3 Half fill the basin with cold water; add 1 tsp salt.

4 Using the peeler, or knife if preferred, peel the potatoes including any 'eyes' or discoloured parts. Put the potatoes in the salted water. Fig. 2.

Fig. 2

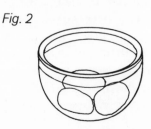

5 Weigh the peelings; wrap in paper and throw away.

6 Half fill the saucepan with cold water, bring to boiling point on a high heat.

7 Drain the potatoes, cut them into even sized pieces if very large, and carefully place them in the boiling water.

8 Add 1 tsp salt, put the lid on the pan and keep the water boiling for about 20 min.

9 Grease the pie dish with some of the margarine and grate the cheese.

10 Test the boiled potatoes with the point of the vegetable knife. When cooked (i.e. soft) drain them over a sink. Fig. 3.

11 Mash the potatoes in the pan with the rest of the margarine and about three-quarters of the cheese.

12 Put the potato mixture into the pie dish and press it down with a fork. Fig. 4.

13 Sprinkle the remaining cheese over the top of the potato.

14 Brown the top of the pie under a hot grill.

15 Wash up.

Fig. 3

Fig. 4

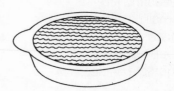

Questions

1 Did the potatoes lose any weight when scrubbed?

2 How heavy were the clean potatoes?

3 How heavy were the peeled potatoes?

4 How much 'rubbish' was removed from the potatoes when they were peeled?

5 Were the potato peelings very thin? If not, why not?

6 What is the price of potatoes?

7 About how much did the peelings cost?

8 Is it worth paying extra for potatoes which are sold (a) washed (b) in polythene bags? If so, give reasons.

9 Potatoes can be baked in their skins. What are the advantages of this method of cooking them?

10 What can be served with a cheese and potato pie to make it part of an interesting meal?

Further work

1 A lot of people in this country eat potatoes every day. Make a list of all the different ways in which potatoes can be cooked.

2 Find some interesting recipes which include potatoes in their list of ingredients.

3 Compare the cost of potatoes in local shops, supermarkets, markets and roadside stalls.

4 Make a list of other foods which have inedible parts.

5 Describe the tools which are available to remove the inedible parts of vegetables and fruits.

6 Find out about different types of kitchen scales. Compare their prices.

How do you think you could waste less when using potatoes?

9 How can you prevent peeled apples from going brown?

When they are peeled or cut up many vegetables and fruits go discoloured. Chemicals in the food, called enzymes, cause these changes. The enzymes must be destroyed if the food is not to be spoiled.

Collect

kettle
measuring jug
6 small basins or jam jars
2 plates
chopping board
vegetable peeler

vegetable knife
apple corer (optional)
teaspoon
salt
vinegar

lemon juice
sugar
an apple
12 scraps of paper for labels
washing-up equipment

Method

1 Boil some water in the kettle and put 200 ml in one of the basins.

Fig. 1

2 Put 200 ml cold water in each of the other five basins.

3 Prepare labels for the basins: Hot Water, Cold Water, Salt, Sugar, Lemon Juice, Vinegar. Fig. 1.

4 Add 1 tsp of salt, sugar, lemon juice or vinegar to the appropriate basin.

5 Prepare labels for the plates: Untreated, Salt, Sugar, Lemon Juice, Vinegar, Cold.

Fig. 2

6 Remove the core, then peel the apple. Cut away any bruised parts.

7 Cut the apple into quarters, then each quarter into 3 slices (making 12 slices).

8 Place one slice in each of the basins. Fig. 2.

9 Place one slice on a plate with the 'cold' label and put into a refrigerator.

10 Arrange the remaining 5 slices round the edge of a second plate and use the prepared labels. Fig. 3.

11 Sprinkle ½ tsp of the substance named on the label over the surface of the appropriate slice.

12 Start the questions.

13 Look at the slices after 10 min, 20 min, 30 min. Make a note of changes, if any, that occur.

14 After 30 min, drain the liquid from the basins.

15 Rinse each of the sprinkled slices separately under the cold tap. Taking care to keep them correctly labelled, place them on the plate with the 'cold' slice.

16 Compare all the slices (both sides) with the 'untreated' one for colour, texture and flavour.

17 Wash up.

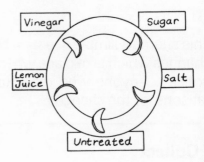

Fig. 3

Questions

1 Prepare a chart so that results can be tabulated:

treatment	colour	texture	flavour

Fill this in after completing the investigation.

2 Which recipes use peeled apples?

3 Why is it necessary to try to stop peeled apples going brown?

4 Which treatment would be the most expensive to use?

5 Was there any difference between the top and underneath sides of the slices left on the plates?

6 From the results, which treatments should be
(a) definitely avoided
(b) most likely to give good results?

7 Which is the simplest and most practical of the effective treatments to use?

Further work

1 Different varieties of apples go brown at different rates. Measure the pH (see Investigation 5) of some varieties and see if there might be any connection between their acidity and the rate of browning.

2 Try the treatments which were found to be effective with apples and see if they prevent peeled potatoes and/or pears going brown.

Which methods did you find best for preventing peeled apples going brown?

10 What happens when milk is boiled?

This seems a simple question but can you really explain what happens? Many of the changes which take place when foods are cooked are so familiar that they are hardly noticed. Anyone who really understands about cooking should be able to give reasons for the changes.

Collect

250 ml milk
milk pan (*not* non-stick)
strainer
measuring jug

2 Pyrex basins
different types of pan scourers
cup and saucer
teaspoon

cocoa or instant coffee
sugar, if liked
washing-up equipment

Method

1 Pour 100 ml milk in a basin.

2 Put 150 ml milk in a pan over a moderate heat. Fig. 1.

3 Watch the milk in the pan very carefully.

4 Remove the pan from the heat as soon as the milk boils.

5 Pour the boiled milk into the second basin.

6 Fill the milky pan with cold water.

7 Compare the hot and cold milk for appearance, smell and flavour.

8 Wash the pan in hot water and washing-up detergent using a dish cloth. Examine the pan carefully.

9 Clean the pan, trying different scourers, rinse and dry it.

10 Note any changes now the boiled milk has cooled. Strain it into the clean pan and re-heat. Taste what is in the strainer. Fig. 2.

Fig. 1

moderate heat

Fig. 2

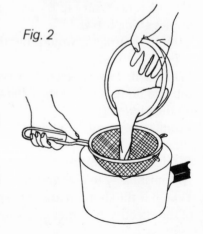

11 Make a cup of cocoa or coffee, drink it. (Do not put cold water in the dirty pan this time.) Fig. 3.

12 Wash up. Clean the pan.

Fig. 3

Questions

1 What changes could be seen as the milk was heated?

2 What differences are there between boiled and unboiled milk?

3 Although milk contains a lot of water, when it reaches boiling point it reacts quite differently to water. How? Why?

4 What is removed from boiled milk by straining? Where has it come from? What does it taste like?

5 What happens to a pan in which milk has been boiled?

6 Does leaving a milky pan full of cold water before washing up make any difference to how easily it is cleaned?

7 Why is some type of pan scourer needed to clean a milky pan?

8 Which type of scourer is the easiest, quickest and most pleasant to use?

Further work

1 Milk pans can be bought with a 'non-stick' lining. Find out how these have been treated and what their advantages and disadvantages are.

2 What are milk pans made from? Find the prices of several different types.

3 Draw a labelled diagram of a well designed milk pan.

4 Find advertisements of products which can be used to make milky drinks. What claims, if any, are made by the manufacturers of these products?

5 Conduct a survey among your friends/classmates/neighbours to see which milky drink is the most popular.

Whenever you are cooking try to notice all the changes that take place and find out what has happened.

Part 2: Fabric

11 What are fibres?

The labels on clothes usually name the fibre, or mixture of fibres, from which the fabric is made. Fibres are very tiny so you have probably never noticed them. If you can see differences between fibres you should begin to understand why, for example, cotton fabrics are different to woollen fabrics.

Collect

a piece of cotton gingham about 5 cm square

a length of woollen knitting yarn about 10 cm long

linen prover or small magnifying glass

sellotape

scissors

ruler

microscope

2 microscope slides and cover slips

Method

1 Examine the gingham and describe what can be seen and felt.

2 Use a magnifying glass. What extra details are now visible? Fig. 1.

3 Carefully take the gingham apart along one side of the square. How strong are the separate strands?

4 Untwist one of the strands and find *one* tiny thread. Fig. 2. Each tiny thread is a FIBRE. How long is it? How strong is it?

5 Using sellotape, stick a few tiny threads, some separate strands and a small piece of gingham on to a sheet of paper using these labels:
Cotton Fibres
Cotton Yarn
Cotton Fabric.

6 Place about three of the cotton fibres on a microscope slide and hold in place with a cover slip. Fig. 3.

7 Draw what can be seen through the microscope.

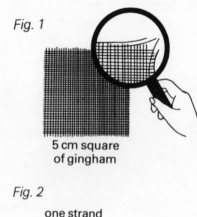

Fig. 1

5 cm square of gingham

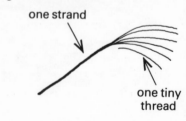

Fig. 2

one strand

one tiny thread

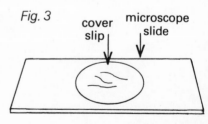

Fig. 3

cover slip

microscope slide

8 Untwist the end of the knitting yarn. Fig. 4. Stick down a few fibres and a short length of yarn on to paper using the labels:
Wool Fibres
Woollen Yarn.

9 Mount a few wool fibres on another slide. Draw what can be seen through the microscope.

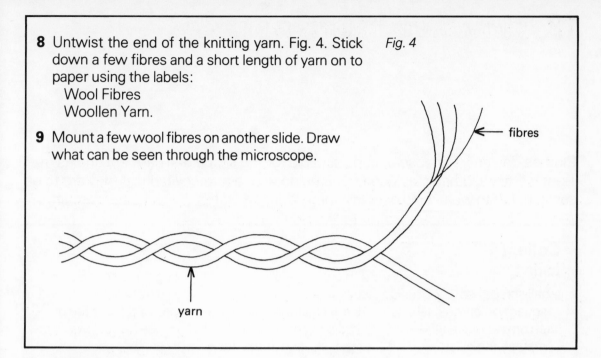

Fig. 4

Questions

1 Describe a single cotton fibre.
2 Cotton fibres come from a plant. Where are cotton plants grown?
3 Describe or draw a cotton plant. In which part of the plant do the fibres grow?
4 How are the fibres removed from a cotton plant?
5 What treatment is needed before cotton fibres can be used to make yarn?
6 Where do wool fibres come from?
7 What are the differences between cotton and wool fibres?
8 What is cotton wool? Why is the name confusing?
9 Name another fibre which comes from a plant.
10 Name another fibre which comes from an animal.
11 What are 'man-made' fibres?
12 Name some man-made fibres that are used in making clothes.

Further work

1 The cotton industry in Great Britain was started in Lancashire. Find out why.
2 What is 'ginning' and how does it get its name?
3 Find out about the connection between slavery and growing cotton.
4 Which breeds of sheep produce the best fibres for clothing?
5 Find out which materials are used in the manufacture of man-made fibres.
6 What is a 'spinneret'?

Read all the labels on your own clothes. See how many different fibres were used to make them.

12 How are fabrics made?

Clothes designers choose a fabric suitable for the shape of a garment and its use. Tightly fitting clothes may need to be made from a stretchy fabric if they are to be comfortable to wear. Find out why some fabrics are stretchy and others are firm.

Collect

scissors
small scraps about 2 cm
   square of 'bit-box' fabrics
linen prover or small
   magnifying glass
microscope

2 microscope slides
sellotape
15 cm square of thick cardboard or an expanded
   polystyrene 'meat' tray
knitting yarn

large eyed needle or
   safety pin
pair of thick knitting
   needles or large
   crochet hook

Method

1 Using the prover or magnifying glass examine the scraps of fabric and sort out into three groups:
   (a) *woven fabrics*: those with two sets of threads at right angles to each other. Fig. 1.
   (b) *knitted fabrics*: those with loops. Fig. 2.
   (c) neither woven nor knitted and 'unidentified'.

2 Use the microscope to see in which group each unidentified' fabric should be placed – each scrap can be held in place between two microscope slides.

3 Using sellotape, stick examples of each group on to paper under their correct heading.

4 Look carefully at your own clothes to see how the fabrics are made.

5 Make a loom with the cardboard or polystyrene tray by cutting notches about 5 mm wide along two opposite edges. Fig. 3.

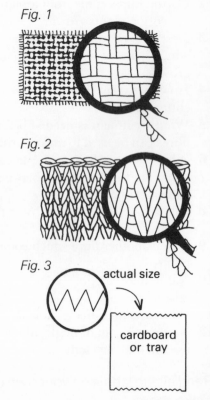

Fig. 1

Fig. 2

Fig. 3

actual size

cardboard
or tray

6 Wind a long length of yarn backwards and forwards round the notches, across the front of the loom, Fig. 4, fastening each end to the back of the loom with sellotape.

7 Thread a needle with another length of yarn or tie it to a safety pin. Pass the needle or pin alternately over and under the yarn fastened on the loom. Fig. 5. At the end of one width, turn round and come back alternately under and over. This makes a simple plain weave. Continue until the loom is full.

8 Try making some fabric from loops using knitting needles or a crochet hook.

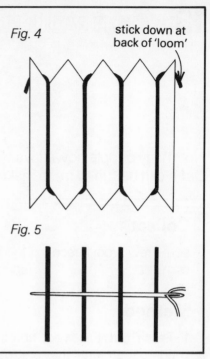

Fig. 4

stick down at back of 'loom'

Fig. 5

Questions

1 What differences are there between woven and knitted fabrics?

2 Which of your clothes are made from (a) woven fabric? (b) knitted fabric?

3 Are you wearing any clothes which are neither woven nor knitted? If so, describe them.

4 Which threads on a loom are called *warp* threads and which ones are called *weft* threads?

5 What is the *selvedge* of a piece of woven fabric?

6 A hole in fabric can be repaired by darning. How is this done?

7 Why do 'ladders' sometimes appear in knitted fabrics?

8 Describe some fabrics which are neither woven nor knitted.

Further work

1 Collect a variety of different threads (e.g. thin string, sewing cotton, ribbon) and experiment with their use on a loom and/or with knitting needles, to make some unusual fabrics.

2 Try weaving to give a patterned effect e.g. using different colours of yarn or going under and over more than one thread on a loom.

3 What are the names of some patterned weaves?

4 Look very carefully at a piece of gingham fabric and explain how the different coloured squares have been made.

5 Find some pictures or diagrams of looms which can be used to make long lengths of wide fabric. What are the names of the various parts of a loom?

6 Find out about portable knitting machines. How much do they cost? What can be knitted on them?

Will clothes made from woven fabrics keep their shape better than knitted fabrics? If so, why?

13 Can you make some fabric?

Not many people nowadays would want to make all the fabric for their own needs. But it can be fun to try to make a few small pieces.

Collect

some raw wool fleece
comb

1 m knitting yarn
spindle (or make one) Fig. 2.

15 cm square of thick cardboard or an expanded polystyrene 'meat' tray

Method

1 Tease out the wool fibres with fingertips or comb them until they are roughly parallel. Fig. 1.

2 Use a spindle, or make one. Fig. 2. Tie the knitting yarn on to it, starting at A. Loop the yarn round the hook with a half hitch. Fig. 2B. There should be about 20 cm of yarn left above the hook to suspend the spindle: break off any surplus.

3 Hold the combed fleece in one hand and gently draw out an end about 10 cm long.

4 Overlap this end with the end of the yarn on the spindle and hold between thumb and finger. Fig. 3.

5 Twist the spindle sharply, like a top, and let it spin until there is a tight twist below thumb and finger. Slowly release the thumb and finger and the twist will join the two ends.

6 Gradually draw out more fibres from the combed fleece, repeat the twisting of the spindle and allow the twist to move up the fibres, spinning them into yarn.

7 When the spun yarn is so long that the spindle is near the floor, unhook it, wind some of it round the spindle shaft at A and re-thread the spindle.

8 Use the yarn to make a piece of woven fabric (see page 30).

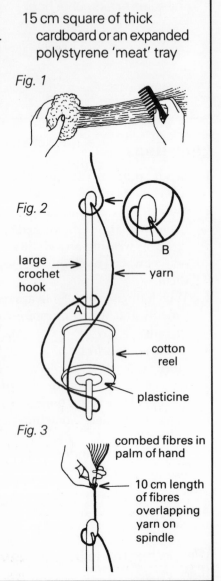

Fig. 1

Fig. 2

large crochet hook

yarn

B

A

cotton reel

plasticine

Fig. 3

combed fibres in palm of hand

10 cm length of fibres overlapping yarn on spindle

Fig. 4

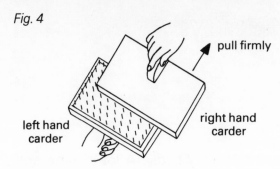

pull firmly

left hand carder

right hand carder

Fig. 5

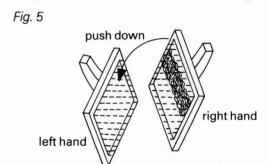

push down

left hand

right hand

Questions

1 Describe the yarn and fabric you have made.
2 Why do raw wool fibres feel greasy?
3 Why is it easier to spin yarn from wool before it is washed?
4 Why is it necessary to comb the fibres before spinning yarn?
5 Why is spinning with a spindle only suitable for fairly short lengths of yarn?
6 How is hand spun yarn different from machine spun yarn?
7 What is 2-ply yarn? How could it be made?
8 What is a spinning wheel? How does it work? When was it invented?
9 Which methods, other than weaving, could be used to make the yarn you have spun into fabric? Try some of them.
10 Fibres are very small and weak. How does fabric made from fibres get its strength?

Further work

1 Use carders to prepare raw wool fleece for spinning.
   (a) Pull wool fleece apart with fingers to remove any hard bits and loosen the fibres.
   (b) Hold carders as in Fig. 4, placing a small handful of wool on left hand carder.
   (c) Draw right hand carder firmly from left hand carder several times until all wool is transferred to right hand carder.
   (d) Turn carders to position in Fig. 5, holding right hand higher than left. Return wool to left hand carder by pushing right hand carder down on to it.
   (e) Repeat (b) to (d) twice more.
   (f) Lift left hand higher than right and push carder down to transfer wool to right hand carder, then back to left hand carder as before. Repeat this movement several times until wool can be lifted off the carder in one sheet.
   (g) Roll the wool into a 'sausage' between the backs of the carders.
2 What is the proper name of the 'sausage'?
3 Does carding prepare the fibres for spinning better than combing? (Try spinning some carded wool.)
4 Where in the British Isles is hand spinning and weaving still done?
5 Find out about the famous people who developed the spinning and weaving industry in this country.

If you managed to make a piece of fabric from some fibres it is unique. No one else can have made a piece exactly the same!

14 Does it crease easily?

It can be very disappointing when clothes crease very badly. A lot of time and energy can be wasted ironing creased fabric. So which fibres make fabrics which do not crease easily?

Collect

10 cm squares of uncreased woven and knitted fabrics made from different fibres (e.g. cotton, wool, nylon, polyester)

scissors
ball point pen
some heavy weights
a flat board or large book
pins

a string clothes line (e.g. tied between 2 chairs)
electric iron
ironing board

Method

1 Cut each piece of fabric into two equal strips, A and B. Use the pen to label the corner of each strip.

Fig. 1

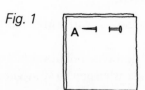

2 Fold all the A strips into half and hold in place with a pin. Fig. 1.

3 Place the folded strips on a flat surface, cover them with the flat board and place weights on top. Fig. 2. Leave for 10 minutes.

Fig. 2

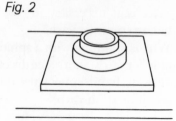

4 Screw up a B strip of fabric tightly, in one hand. Count to ten slowly. Release the fabric. Pin it on the clothes line by one end. Fig. 3.

5 Describe the creasing: none, very little, moderate, rather bad, very bad.

Fig. 3

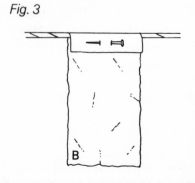

6 Repeat 4 and 5 for all the B strips.

7 Pin the A strips on the line and describe the fold line: invisible, slightly visible, clearly seen, very noticeable.

8 Set the iron at cool.

9 Unpin the A strips and refold them. Iron across the folds. Repeat 7.

10 Unpin all the strips and iron them flat.

11 If any strips are still creased, re-set the iron to warm 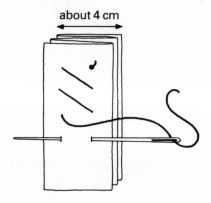 and iron them again.

12 If any creases still remain, try pressing over a damp cloth or on the 'steam' setting of an iron.

Questions

1 Which fabrics creased least?

2 Which fabrics creased most?

3 Did the fabrics which creased badly in a warm hand all crease badly under a heavy weight?

4 Did any creases disappear, or become less noticeable, when the strips had been hanging up for a while?

5 Did the woven fabrics crease more or less than the knitted fabrics?

6 Were the ironed fold lines as easy to remove as other creases?

7 Starting with the least easily creased, list the fibres in the samples of fabrics investigated in order of 'creaseability'.

8 When wearing clothes what is likely to cause creasing?

9 What are the advantages of wearing clothes made from fabrics which do not crease easily?

10 When choosing new clothes how can their 'creaseability' be decided?

Fig. 4

about 4 cm

Further work

1 Some fabrics are made from mixtures of fibres. Make a list of mixtures used for clothing and bedding fabrics. Think of some reasons why fibres are mixed in this way.

2 Permanent creases (e.g. in trousers and pleats) can be desirable. Try to make some:
 (a) Fold a 20 cm × 10 cm piece of woven nylon or polyester fabric into accordian pleats and tack in place. Fig. 4.
 (b) Using a warm 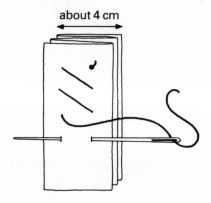 iron, cover the pleated fabric with thin paper and press very firmly.
 (c) Remove the tacking, wash the fabric and drip-dry it.
 (d) If the pleats have washed out, repeat (a) to (c) using a hotter iron.

3 Fabrics which can be permanently pleated by heat are called 'thermoplastic'. Were any of the fabrics tested thermoplastic?

4 Why is it very important to use the correct iron setting when removing creases from fabrics?

5 Find out how fabrics which are not thermoplastic are permanently creased.

6 Some fabrics which normally crease badly are made 'crease-resistant'. How and why is this done?

How can you help to keep new clothes looking smart and fresh?

15 Does it absorb perspiration easily?

By perspiring, the body loses over half a litre of water every day. Unless clothes next to the skin soak up this liquid, they can be uncomfortable to wear. In hot weather and for very active people, such as athletes, it is particularly important that clothes should be absorbent.

Collect

12 cm × 3 cm strips of uncreased woven and knitted fabrics made from different fibres (e.g. wool, cotton, nylon, polyester)

deep washing-up bowl
1 m string
pins
wire cooling tray
ruler

jug
knitting pin or skewer
paper towels

Method

1 Attach the strips of fabric to the string by folding over 1 cm and pinning as shown. Fig. 1. The strips MUST be the same length.

Fig. 1

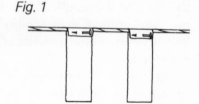

2 Tie the string tightly round the cooling tray to suspend the strips below the mesh. Support the string in the centre with a knot. Fig. 2.

3 Balance the tray over the bowl. The strips must not touch each other. Slowly pour sufficient water into the bowl so that the ends of the fabric strips are just under the surface of the water. Fig. 3. If any of the strips curl upwards gently uncurl them with the end of the knitting pin so they remain in the water.

Fig. 2

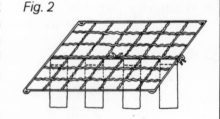

4 After 5 min lift off the tray. Measure the distance the water has travelled up each strip. Hold the tray up to the light if the water level is not easy to see.

Fig. 3

5 Put the tray back over the water for 10 min. Measure the water levels again.

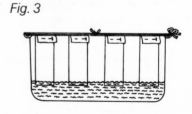

6 Unpin one of the strips, shake it to remove any drips of water and place it inside a folded paper towel. Press it hard to remove as much water as possible. Fig. 4.

Fig. 4

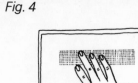
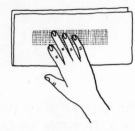

7 Repeat 6 for each strip. Compare the size of the wet blobs on the towels.

8 Feel each strip of fabric. Arrange them in order of how wet they feel.

Questions

1 Which fabric soaked up water the quickest?

2 Which of the fabrics did not have a clear line to show the water level?

3 Which fabric soaked up the most water?

4 Which fabric soaked up the least water?

5 Which wet fabrics felt the coldest?

6 Which wet fabrics felt the warmest?

7 Which fabrics would make the best clothes to wear in hot weather? Why?

8 Which fabrics would make the most uncomfortable clothes to wear in hot weather?

9 Will the fabrics that soaked up the most water take the longest to dry?

10 Do some fabrics soak up more water than others because of their construction or because they are made from different fibres?

Further work

1 If the answer to Question 10 was guessed, check it by re-doing this investigation using fabrics chosen specially to make comparisons:

e.g. (a) thin woven cotton poplin and thick woven cotton denim.

(b) thin knitted cotton fabric and thin knitted nylon fabric.

2 Explain why athletes should put on a track suit after completing energetic activities.

3 Describe the various ways in which moisture can be removed from wet fabrics.

4 Why is it essential that clothes are completely dry before they are folded up and put away?

5 Find out how fabric can be treated to prevent it absorbing moisture and explain the differences between 'showerproof' and 'waterproof' fabrics.

Describe the best types of fabric for games wear.

16 Why do clothes get dirty?

It is easy to see that mud and spilt food make clothes dirty. But why do some fabrics look 'grubby' more quickly than others? Perhaps there are some less obvious reasons that you can discover.

Collect

scraps of fabric with different surfaces (e.g. smooth,
   rough, fluffy)
magnifying glass
flour
teaspoon

clothes brush
tissue paper
20 cm × 10 cm pieces of
   fabrics made from different fibres (e.g. cotton,
   wool, nylon, polyester)

paper punch
plastic pen
damp paper towel
kettle of hot water
laundry tongs

Method

1 Look at the surface of the scraps of fabric through the magnifying glass. Decide which are smooth, slightly rough, hairy, very fluffy. Fig. 1.

Fig. 1

2 Sprinkle about ¼ tsp flour on each of the scraps and rub it in with the back of the spoon. Fig. 2. Shake each piece (over a waste bin) and note which still have flour clinging to them.

3 Brush vigorously and re-examine.

Fig. 2

4 Make some confetti with tissue paper and a paper punch.

5 Put 6 pieces of confetti on a flat surface. Wipe the plastic pen once with the damp paper towel. Check that it will not 'pick up' the confetti when held over, but not actually touching, the paper. Fig. 3.

Fig. 3

6 Rub the pen vigorously with one of the rectangles of fabric while counting 10. Hold the rubbed part of the fabric over the confetti.

7 If the fabric does not 'pick up' the confetti, see if the pen does. If the fabric does pick it up proceed as follows:

Fig. 4

  (a) Remove the confetti and throw it away.
  (b) Boil some water so that a stream of steam is leaving the kettle spout.
  (c) Using laundry tongs, hold the fabric in the steam for 2 seconds. Fig. 4.
  (d) Hold the steamed fabric over some more confetti and note what happens.

8 Repeat 5, 6, 7 for each rectangle of fabric.

9 Try to pick up confetti with fabrics which have been rubbed against (a) themselves (b) each other.

Questions

1 Which type of surface trapped most flour?
2 Which fabrics would trap most dust from the air?
3 Which types of fabric might stay clean longest under similar conditions?
4 Which rubbed fabrics picked up the confetti?
5 Which rubbed fabrics did not pick up the confetti?
6 Did the fabrics made from natural fibres (e.g. cotton) pick up the confetti more easily or less easily than those made from 'man-made' fibres (e.g. nylon)?
7 What effect did steaming have on the rubbed fabrics?
8 Where do fabrics rub together in use?
9 Why do some clothes 'pick up' dirt more easily than others?
10 Why is a clothes brush sometimes not very good for removing dust from clothes?

Further work

1 The rubbing together of the fabric and plastic pen produced a form of electricity, called *static electricity*, which attracted the confetti. Think of some more examples where surfaces cling together by static electricity.
2 When is static electricity, produced by fabrics, likely to be most troublesome in a home?
3 'Fabric conditioners' make fabrics feel softer and bulkier by reducing static electricity. Find out how they are used. Try to decide whether they are worth the time and money spent on them.
4 Where does dust in the air, which can be attracted to clothes by static electricity, come from? Think of ways in which the amount of dust in the air can be kept low.

How can clothes be prevented from getting dirty too quickly?

17 Is water really wet?

Washing is the most usual method of getting dirty clothes clean. But does water always wet fabric? Unless it does, washing will not be a very good cleaning method. Find out how to make water really wet!

Collect

15 cm × 5 cm scraps of clean, new fabric of different types and thicknesses
glass rod

teaspoon
bowl or jug of cold water
liquid detergent e.g. Stergene

powder detergent e.g. Persil
paper towel

Method

1 Let 4 single drops of water fall from a glass rod on to the surface of a piece of fabric. The drops should be evenly spaced. Fig. 1.

Fig. 1

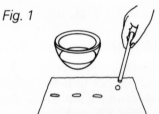

2 If the water soaks into the fabric repeat 1 with other fabrics. Find a fabric on which the water remains in drops.

3 Look very carefully at the drops of water and describe them.

Fig. 2

4 Using the glass rod, stir and rub one of the drops until it soaks into the fabric.

5 Using the handle of the spoon, pour 1 single drop of liquid detergent on to the second water drop. Watch carefully what happens. Fig. 2.

6 Sprinkle a very tiny pinch of dry detergent powder on to the third water drop. Fig. 3.

Fig. 3

7 Pick up the fabric with one corner, gently shake it and see what happens to the fourth drop of water.

8 Dry the work surface and repeat 1, 4, 5, 6 and 7 with remaining samples of fabric.

Fig. 4

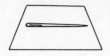

Fig. 5

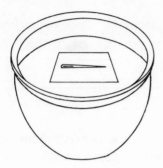

Questions

1 Which fabrics were easily wetted by water?

2 Which fabrics were not wetted at all by water alone?

3 What shape are the drops of water which do not soak into fabric?

4 How can water be made to wet fabric?

5 Which is the quickest way?

6 Which is the best way? Why?'

7 What actually happens to drops of water when they are made to wet fabric?

8 Does warm water wet fabric more easily than cold? Try it!

9 What is usually done to washing powders before they are used? Why?

10 Why is it essential that water should really wet clothes that are being washed?

Further work

1 When water remains in drops on the surface of a fabric it is showing *surface tension*. It is as though each drop has an invisible skin round it. Try floating a needle on water:

   (a) Place a small, clean sewing needle on a square of thin blotting paper. Fig. 4.

   (b) Carefully place the blotting paper on the surface of a bowl of cold water. Fig. 5.

   (c) Leave undisturbed: the blotting paper should fall to the bottom of the bowl (why?), the needle should remain floating on the water (why?).

2 Explain why it might have been necessary in Investigation 15 to use a knitting pin to push the ends of some strips of fabric under the surface of the water.

3 In Method 4 did the 'stirred' drops of water soak into all the fabric samples at the same speed? If not, see if the slowest or fastest are similar to the fabrics in Investigation 15 which absorbed water slowly or quickly.

4 Surface tension between water and fabric does not make a fabric waterproof. Explain why not. See what happens when the surface of a fabric is coated with any of the following: Vaseline, candle wax, cooking oil, wax floor polish. Giving reasons, decide whether any of these treatments would be suitable for making a fabric waterproof.

5 Dry one of the fabric strips used in this investigation and repeat the Method. Use the results obtained to explain why clothes made from fabric which has been treated to make it 'showerproof' or 'waterproof' MUST be rinsed very thoroughly after washing.

Think of some examples of where you would not want water to wet fabric easily.

18 Why are detergents used to clean dirty clothes?

You may have discovered one reason in Investigation 17. Grease and oil – from food, skin and dirty jobs – may be difficult to wash out of clothes. See how detergents can help.

Collect

cotton fabric (e.g. gingham or calico) cut into 6 × 5 cm squares
4 basins, 4 teaspoons
measuring jug

2 small plates
6 scraps of paper for labels
small dropper or glass rod
pencil
cooking oil

powder detergent e.g. Surf
2 paper towels
pins
iron and ironing board
washing-up equipment

Method

1 Prepare paper labels: 1. Untreated, 2. Dry Detergent, 3. Cold Water, 4. Hot Water, 5. Cold Water and Detergent, 6. Hot Water and Detergent.

2 Using the dropper, put 2 drops of oil in the centre of each fabric square. Fig. 1.

3 Put one square on a plate, label it 'Untreated'.

4 Put one square on another plate, sprinkle 1 tsp of powder detergent over the fabric. Label it 'Dry Detergent.' Fig. 2.

5 Put 100 ml cold water in each of 2 basins.

6 Put 100 ml hot water (from tap) in each of 2 basins.

7 Stir 1 tsp powder detergent into one of the basins of cold water.

8 Stir 1 tsp powder detergent into one of the basins of hot water.

9 Stand each basin with a teaspoon in it on its correct label.

10 Put a square of fabric in each basin and stir vigorously for about 5 seconds. Fig. 3.

Fig. 1

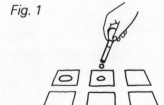

Fig. 2

Fig. 3

Fig. 4

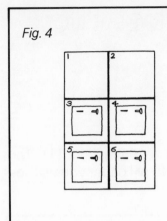

11 Draw lines on one of the paper towels to make six 'boxes'; number them 1 to 6.

12 Lift the fabric out of the water, touching only one corner. Shake off any drops of water and place fabric flat on the towel in the correct box.

13 Put to dry in a warm place. The fabric can be pinned to the paper if necessary. Fig. 4.

14 Shake the powder detergent off the 'Dry Detergent' square. Put it and the 'untreated' one in the correct boxes.

15 Compare all the samples with the 'Untreated' one. Answer Questions 1 to 3.

16 Set the iron at warm ◿▱ . Cover the six samples with another paper towel and press the 'sandwich' firmly with the iron. Remove the fabric; inspect the papers.

Fig. 5

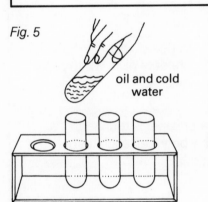

oil and cold water

Questions

1 Which treatment, if any, had no effect on the oily fabric?

2 Which fabrics (a) looked (b) felt and (c) smelt oily after treatment?

3 Which treatment cleaned the fabric best?
Now complete Method 16.

4 Why were there oily patches on the paper after ironing?

5 Were all the oily patches under the fabric squares the same? If not, why not?

6 Had the treatment which seemed to clean the fabric best (Q. 3) removed all the oil? If so, where had it gone?

7 Did dry powder detergent remove the oil? If not, why not?

8 Why are both water and a detergent needed to wash greasy clothes?

Further work

1 Set up the equipment as in Investigation 1: Further work (p. 7). Carry out the experiment using Stergene or a solution of a powder detergent. Explain what happens to greasy dirt when clothes are washed in a detergent solution.

2 Oil and water do not normally mix. When they do they form an *emulsion*. Set up an experiment to show how a detergent can make an emulsion of oil and water. Fig. 5 may be a good way to start.

3 Cooking oil is only one likely cause of greasy marks on clothing. Make a list of other possible sources. Which parts of clothes are most likely to get greasy?

4 Find out about the aerosol laundry sprays that can be used on greasy marks before dirty clothes are washed (e.g. Frend). Where might they be useful?

5 Some fabrics must not be washed. How can *dry cleaning fluids* be used to remove greasy marks from unwashable clothes?

How do washing machines get clothes clean?

19 Which detergents are best for washing woollens?

Wool fibres have delicate overlapping scales (remember Investigation 11). The scales can be damaged by alkaline chemicals. By testing with pH paper you will see which detergents are the safest to use.

Collect

a selection of detergents including some which claim to 'wash whiter' and some for 'delicate fabrics'

teaspoon
basin
pH indicator paper with colour chart

paper towels
sheet of plain white paper
pins

WARNINGS: Hands MUST BE DRY every time the indicator paper is touched.
Spoon and bowl must be RINSED thoroughly between each test.

Method

1 Prepare a chart on the plain paper.

detergent	indicator paper	pH

Fig. 1

2 Mix 1 tsp detergent with 4 tsp cold water in the basin.

3 Take a piece of indicator paper and dip one end in the detergent solution. Fig. 1.

Fig. 2

4 Compare the colour of the wet end of the paper with the colour chart and decide the pH. Pin the indicator paper to the chart and fill in the details.

5 Rinse the basin and spoon, dry the spoon.

6 Repeat 2, 3 and 4 for each detergent.

7 Test the pH of tap water: hot and cold. Fig. 2.

Fig. 3

Questions

1–6	pH 7	8–14
increasingly ← acidic		→ increasingly alkaline

1 Using the chart above, make a list of the detergents tested in order of their pH, starting with the most alkaline.

2 What is the word that would describe a detergent which is neither an acid nor an alkali (i.e. pH 7)?

3 Which detergents were not alkaline?

4 Which detergents had the lowest alkaline pH?

5 What is the pH of water?

6 Does the temperature of the water make any difference to the pH of a detergent solution?

7 Is the pH of a weak (dilute) detergent solution the same as the pH of a strong (concentrated) detergent solution? Test it.

8 Alkaline chemicals damage wool fibres. Name the detergents which are best for washing woollen clothes.

Further work

1 Read the slogans on detergent packets. Fig. 3. Sort out those which claim to improve the 'whiteness' of washing. Are the pH readings of these detergents similar? What sort of 'whitener' might they have in them?

2 What claims are made for the detergents which do not mention whiteness? Are their pH readings similar?

3 Explain why the following 'rules' should be followed when washing clothes:
(a) Read the labels on the clothes.
(b) Use the correct quantity of detergent as stated on the packet.
(c) Dissolve the detergent in water before adding the clothes.
(d) Rinse clothes thoroughly.
(e) Rinse hands after using detergents.

4 Conduct a survey among friends and neighbours to find out favourite washing products. Ask for the reasons for their choice.

5 Skin, as well as wool, should be protected from strongly alkaline chemicals. Find the 'gentlest' toilet soap and hair shampoo by testing pH.

Why are the detergents which claim to wash 'whiter than white' not very suitable for woollens?

20 What is it?

An unlabelled fabric or knitting yarn can be difficult to identify. You can guess by comparing with labelled samples but a more accurate answer should be obtained from this experiment.

Collect

retort stand, boss and metal rod
baking tray
2 large bulldog clips
ruler

2 cm × 15 cm strips of known fabrics (e.g. cotton, wool, nylon, polyester)
2 cm × 15 cm strips of fabric to be identified

60 cm lengths of several knitting yarns including one labelled '100% wool'
matches
wax tapers

For SAFETY have ready a jug of water as a fire extinguisher and hold long hair back with rubber bands.

Fig. 1

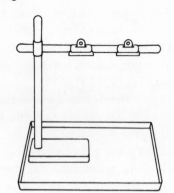

Method

1 Set up equipment. Fig. 1

2 Suspend a strip of a known fabric with one of the bulldog clips.

3 Suspend a 'similar' unidentified fabric with the other clip, leaving at least 15 cm space between the strips.

4 Hold a lighted taper so that the flame is about 5 cm below the known fabric. Fig. 2.

Fig. 2

5 Watch the fabric very carefully and slowly move the flame towards it. Hold the taper steady when its flame is touching the fabric. If the fabric starts to burn remove the taper. (Put out the taper but do NOT blow it out towards the burning fabric).

6 Note all that happens and answer Questions 1 to 9.

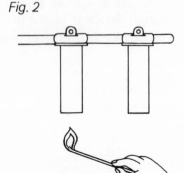

7 Repeat 4, 5 and 6 with the 'similar' unidentified fabric. Answer Question 10.

Fig. 3

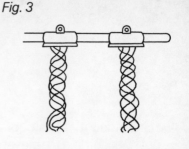

8 Continue comparing strips until the ones to be identified have been matched with known fabrics.

9 Twist the knitting yarns into 15 cm skeins.

10 Compare all the yarns with the '100% wool' sample, by repeating the burning tests. Fig. 3.

Questions

1 Did heat affect the fabric before the flame touched it? If so, how?
2 Did the fabric catch fire? Slowly? Quickly?
3 Did the fabric continue to burn when the taper was removed?
4 What colour was the flame?
5 Was there any smell? If so, describe it.
6 Was there any smoke? If so, what colour?
7 Did the fabric melt?
8 Did the burning fabric drip?
9 What was left?
10 Were the two strips made from the same fibre?
11 Could any of the unmatched fabrics be made from a mixture of fibres?
12 Why is it misleading to call all knitting yarn 'wool'?

Further work

1 If there were some 'unknown' fabrics after completing the burning tests, see if they can be identified by reading a book on *textiles*.
2 Look up the meaning of *inflammable* in a dictionary. Why are fabrics which burn easily more often called *flammable* nowadays?
3 Find out how the law helps to protect young children from injuries caused by burning clothes.
4 Explain the meaning of the international clothes care labels. Fig. 4.
5 What are the 'wash-tub' codes? Why are there so many and where are they used?

Fig. 4

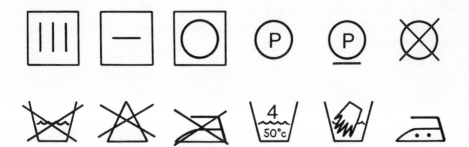

This is not an investigation you could carry out in a shop. But unless you know what a fabric is made from, you will have no idea how to care for it. So whenever you are choosing clothes, or fabric to make clothes, insist on knowing what you are buying.

Notes for teachers

It is not intended that this book should be used as a course of lessons. Investigations may be selected according to relevant criteria in a particular school context and carried out in any order. It is envisaged that the activities could be carried out in upper primary classes, middle schools and the early years of secondary schools. No specialist Home Economics facilities are required for most of the investigations although it is assumed that a water supply is available.

Most of the recording of observations and results can be done in whatever way is preferred. Many of the 'Questions' can be answered verbally if this is an appropriate method for particular pupils or if lessons are short. 'Further Work' is planned to stimulate ideas arising from the activities but does not have to be completed before proceeding to other topics. Although there are a few cross references made in some 'Further work' sections, they are not an essential part of the investigations.

Each 'Investigation' occupies two facing pages so that the opened book can be placed inside a transparent wallet or polythene bag and no turning over of pages is necessary as work proceeds. If a book stand is used further protection is provided. Improvisation is possible when the stated equipment is not available. Empty cottage cheese or yoghurt cartons can be used as basins. Inverted lids of screw top jars make saucers. A rolling pin and unbreakable plastic basin can be substituted for a mortar and pestle. A portable electric hotplate could be used as an alternative to a cooker hob.

The authors believe that an investigatory approach is appropriate to many areas of work in Home Economics and particularly when introducing the materials to be used in the traditional craft aspects of the subject, hence the sub-sections of 'Food' and 'Fabric'. Investigations in this book can precede, accompany or follow the use of such materials with whole classes, groups, pairs or individuals involved. Some of the apparently simple questions posed are not quite so simple to answer — and may have to be left open-ended — but pupils who attempt the investigations in this book are being encouraged to follow instructions correctly and to make accurate observations, both of which are essential skills in the execution of all practical work.